Why Do My Feet Say YES When My Head Says NO?

Eileen L. Cooley Ph.D.
illustrated by Jill Dubin

Headline Kids
an imprint of Headline Books, Inc.

Terra Alta, WV

Why Do My Feet Say YES When My Head Says NO?

by Eileen L. Cooley Ph.D.
illustrated by Jill Dubin

Headline Kids
P. O. Box 52
Terra Alta, WV 26764
www.headlinekids.com

Tel: 800-570-5951
Email: mybook@headlinebooks.com
www.headlinebooks.com
www.headlinekids.com

Published by Headline Books

Headline Kids is an imprint of Headline Books

ISBN-13: 978-0-938467-06-9

Library of Congress Cataloging-in-Publication Data

Cooley, Eileen L.
  Why do my feet say yes when my head says no? / Eileen L. Cooley ; illustrated by Jill Dubin.
    p. cm.
  ISBN 978-0-938467-06-9
  1. Interpersonal relations. 2. Social skills. I. Title.
  HM1106.C665 2011
  646.7'60834--dc22
                          2011000055

PRINTED IN THE UNITED STATES OF AMERICA

To my mother, Selma,
and to Dave, Dana,
and Michael
—ELC

To Clark, Henry,
and Nina
—JD

To all child readers
and their daily dilemmas

My feet say, "I want to jump off the diving board!"

But my head says, "Oh, no. The board is so high."

I know...
"I will jump off the side of the pool first."

My hands say, "I'm so mad I could hit her."

But my head says,
"I'm not supposed to hit other people."

I know...
"I will tell her how mad I am."

My body says, "I want to stay in bed and sleep."

But my head says, "Oh no—it's time to get up."

I know...
"If I get up I can play with my dog!"

My tummy says, "I want to eat this candy."

But my head says,
"Mommy says don't eat before dinner."

I know...
"I will save the candy for dessert."

19

My feet say, "I want to ride the new bicycle."

But my head says, "*I might fall.*"

I know...
"I will get my older sister to hold the bike."

My feet say, "I want to play with Sam and his truck."

But my head says, "I'm afraid he'll say no."

I know...
"I will ask Sam. If he says no, I will play with Emma."

My eyes say, "This video game is so exciting!"

But my head says, "It's bath time and I have to stop."

I know...
"I can play with my toys in the bath."